paperblanks®
PLANNERS

paperblanks®

PLANNER

2 0 2 3

paperblanks®
PLANNERS

NAME _____

PHONE _____

IN CASE OF EMERGENCY, PLEASE CONTACT

NAME _____

PHONE _____

2023

JANUARY

M	T	W	T	F	S	**S**
26	27	28	29	30	31	**1**
2	3	4	5	6	7	**8**
9	10	11	12	13	14	**15**
16	17	18	19	20	21	**22**
23/30	24/31	25	26	27	28	**29**

FEBRUARY

M	T	W	T	F	S	**S**
30	31	1	2	3	4	**5**
6	7	8	9	10	11	**12**
13	14	15	16	17	18	**19**
20	21	22	23	24	25	**26**
27	28	1	2	3	4	5

MARCH

M	T	W	T	F	S	**S**
27	28	1	2	3	4	**5**
6	7	8	9	10	11	**12**
13	14	15	16	17	18	**19**
20	21	22	23	24	25	**26**
27	28	29	30	31	1	2

APRIL

M	T	W	T	F	S	**S**
27	28	29	30	31	1	**2**
3	4	5	6	7	8	**9**
10	11	12	13	14	15	**16**
17	18	19	20	21	22	**23**
24	25	26	27	28	29	**30**

MAY

M	T	W	T	F	S	**S**
1	2	3	4	5	6	**7**
8	9	10	11	12	13	**14**
15	16	17	18	19	20	**21**
22	23	24	25	26	27	**28**
29	30	31	1	2	3	4

JUNE

M	T	W	T	F	S	**S**
29	30	31	1	2	3	**4**
5	6	7	8	9	10	**11**
12	13	14	15	16	17	**18**
19	20	21	22	23	24	**25**
26	27	28	29	30	1	2

JULY

M	T	W	T	F	S	**S**
26	27	28	29	30	1	**2**
3	4	5	6	7	8	**9**
10	11	12	13	14	15	**16**
17	18	19	20	21	22	**23**
24/31	25	26	27	28	29	**30**

AUGUST

M	T	W	T	F	S	**S**
31	1	2	3	4	5	**6**
7	8	9	10	11	12	**13**
14	15	16	17	18	19	**20**
21	22	23	24	25	26	**27**
28	29	30	31	1	2	3

SEPTEMBER

M	T	W	T	F	S	**S**
28	29	30	31	1	2	**3**
4	5	6	7	8	9	**10**
11	12	13	14	15	16	**17**
18	19	20	21	22	23	**24**
25	26	27	28	29	30	1

OCTOBER

M	T	W	T	F	S	**S**
25	26	27	28	29	30	**1**
2	3	4	5	6	7	**8**
9	10	11	12	13	14	**15**
16	17	18	19	20	21	**22**
23/30	24/31	25	26	27	28	**29**

NOVEMBER

M	T	W	T	F	S	**S**
30	31	1	2	3	4	**5**
6	7	8	9	10	11	**12**
13	14	15	16	17	18	**19**
20	21	22	23	24	25	**26**
27	28	29	30	1	2	3

DECEMBER

M	T	W	T	F	S	**S**
27	28	29	30	1	2	**3**
4	5	6	7	8	9	**10**
11	12	13	14	15	16	**17**
18	19	20	21	22	23	**24**
25	26	27	28	29	30	**31**

LEGEND FOR SYMBOLS

Moon Phases

☽ FIRST QUARTER
☾ LAST QUARTER
○ FULL MOON
● NEW MOON

✽ FIRST DAY OF SPRING
🍂 FIRST DAY OF AUTUMN
☀ SHORTEST DAY
☀ LONGEST DAY
🕐 DAYLIGHT SAVING TIME BEGINS/ENDS

INTERNATIONAL HOLIDAYS 2023

AUSTRALIA

January 1	New Year's Day
26	Australia Day
April 7	Good Friday
8	Easter Saturday*
9	Easter
10	Easter Monday
25	Anzac Day
June 12	Queen's Birthday*
December 25	Christmas Day
26	Boxing Day

AUSTRIA

January 1	New Year's Day
6	Epiphany
April 7	Good Friday*
9	Easter
10	Easter Monday
May 1	Labour Day
18	Ascension
29	Whit Monday
June 8	Corpus Christi Day
August 15	Assumption
October 26	National Day
November 1	All Saints' Day
December 8	Immaculate Conception
25	Christmas Day
26	St Stephen's Day

BELGIUM

January 1	New Year's Day
April 9	Easter
10	Easter Monday
May 1	Labour Day
18	Ascension
29	Whit Monday
July 21	National Day
August 15	Assumption
November 1	All Saints' Day
11	Armistice Day
December 25	Christmas Day

CANADA

January 1	New Year's Day
February 20	Civic Holiday*
April 7	Good Friday
9	Easter
May 22	Victoria Day
July 1	Canada Day
August 7	Civic Holiday*
September 4	Labour Day
October 9	Thanksgiving Day
November 11	Remembrance Day
December 25	Christmas Day
26	Boxing Day

CZECH REPUBLIC

January 1	New Year's Day
April 7	Good Friday
9	Easter
10	Easter Monday
May 1	May Day
8	Liberation Day
July 5	St Cyril and St Methodius Day
6	Jan Hus Day
September 28	Statehood Day
October 28	Independence Day
November 17	Freedom and Democracy Day
December 24	Christmas Eve
25	Christmas Day
26	Second Christmas Day

FRANCE

January 1	New Year's Day
April 9	Easter
10	Easter Monday
May 1	Labour Day
8	WWII Victory Day
18	Ascension
29	Whit Monday
July 14	National Day
August 15	Assumption
November 1	All Saints' Day
11	Armistice Day
December 25	Christmas Day

GERMANY

January 1	New Year's Day
April 7	Good Friday
9	Easter
10	Easter Monday
May 1	Labour Day
18	Ascension
29	Whit Monday
October 3	Day of German Unity
December 25	Christmas Day
26	Second Christmas Day

IRELAND

January 1	New Year's Day
March 17	St Patrick's Day
April 7	Good Friday
9	Easter
10	Easter Monday
May 1	May Bank Holiday
June 5	June Bank Holiday
August 7	August Bank Holiday
October 30	October Bank Holiday
December 25	Christmas Day
26	St Stephen's Day

INTERNATIONAL HOLIDAYS 2023

ITALY

January 1	New Year's Day
6	Epiphany
April 9	Easter
10	Easter Monday
25	Liberation Day
May 1	Labour Day
June 2	Republic Day
August 15	Assumption
November 1	All Saints' Day
December 8	Immaculate Conception
25	Christmas Day
26	St Stephen's Day

JAPAN

January 1	New Year's Day
9	Coming of Age Day
February 11	National Foundation Day
23	Emperor's Birthday
March 21	Vernal Equinox Day
April 29	Showa Day
May 3	Constitution Memorial Day
4	Greenery Day
5	Children's Day
July 17	Marine Day
August 11	Mountain Day
September 18	Respect for the Aged Day
23	Autumnal Equinox Day
October 9	Sports Day
November 3	Culture Day
23	Labour Thanksgiving Day

NETHERLANDS

January 1	New Year's Day
April 7	Good Friday*
9	Easter
10	Easter Monday
27	King's Birthday
May 5	Liberation Day
18	Ascension
28	Pentecost
29	Whit Monday
December 25	Christmas Day
26	Second Christmas Day

NORWAY

January 1	New Year's Day
April 6	Maundy Thursday
7	Good Friday
9	Easter
10	Easter Monday
May 1	Labour Day
17	Constitution Day
18	Ascension
28	Whit Sunday
29	Whit Monday
December 25	Christmas Day
26	Second Christmas Day

POLAND

January 1	New Year's Day
6	Epiphany
April 9	Easter
10	Easter Monday
May 1	State Holiday
3	Constitution Day
28	Pentecost
June 8	Corpus Christi Day
August 15	Assumption
November 1	All Saints' Day
11	Independence Day
December 25	Christmas Day
26	Second Christmas Day

PORTUGAL

January 1	New Year's Day
February 21	Shrove Tuesday (Carnival)
April 7	Good Friday
9	Easter
25	Liberation Day
May 1	Labour Day
June 8	Corpus Christi Day
10	National Day
August 15	Assumption
October 5	Republic Day
November 1	All Saints' Day
December 1	Independence Day
8	Immaculate Conception
25	Christmas Day

SLOVAKIA

January 1	New Year's Day
	Republic Day
6	Epiphany
April 7	Good Friday
9	Easter
10	Easter Monday
May 1	May Day
8	Victory Day
July 5	St Cyril and St Methodius Day
August 29	Slovak National Uprising Day
September 1	Constitution Day
15	Our Lady of Sorrows Day
November 1	All Saints' Day
17	Freedom and Democracy Day
December 24	Christmas Eve
25	Christmas Day
26	Second Christmas Day

INTERNATIONAL HOLIDAYS 2023

SPAIN

January 1	New Year's Day
6	Epiphany
April 6	Maundy Thursday*
7	Good Friday
May 1	Labour Day
August 15	Assumption
October 12	National Day
November 1	All Saints' Day
December 6	Constitution Day
8	Immaculate Conception
25	Christmas Day

SWEDEN

January 1	New Year's Day
6	Epiphany
April 7	Good Friday
9	Easter
10	Easter Monday
May 1	Labour Day
18	Ascension
28	Pentecost
June 6	National Day
24	Midsummer's Day
November 4	All Saints' Day
December 25	Christmas Day
26	Second Christmas Day

SWITZERLAND

January 1	New Year's Day
April 7	Good Friday*
9	Easter
10	Easter Monday*
May 1	Labour Day*
18	Ascension
29	Whit Monday*
August 1	National Day
December 25	Christmas Day
26	St Stephen's Day*

UNITED KINGDOM

January 1	New Year's Day
2	Second of January*
March 17	St Patrick's Day*
April 7	Good Friday
9	Easter
10	Easter Monday*
May 1	Early May Bank Holiday
29	Spring Bank Holiday
August 7	Summer Bank Holiday*
28	Summer Bank Holiday*
November 30	St Andrew's Day*
December 25	Christmas Day
26	Boxing Day

USA

January 1	New Year's Day
16	Martin Luther King Jr Day
February 20	Presidents' Day
April 9	Easter
May 29	Memorial Day
July 4	Independence Day
September 4	Labour Day
October 9	Columbus Day
November 11	Veterans' Day
23	Thanksgiving Day
December 25	Christmas Day

Not a public holiday/Not a public holiday in all regions.
This table lists commemorative dates. Additional public holidays may precede or follow some dates.
Regional holidays may not be included. This information is provided as a guide only.

NOTES

JANUARY – 2023 MONTH PLANNER

MONDAY	TUESDAY	WEDNESDAY	THURSDAY	FRIDAY	SATURDAY	SUNDAY
26	27	28	29	30 ☽	31	1
2	3	4	5	6 ○	7	8
9	10	11	12	13	14	15 ☾
16	17	18	19	20	21 ●	22
23	24	25	26	27	28 ☽	29
30	31					

FEBRUARY – 2023 MONTH PLANNER

MONDAY	TUESDAY	WEDNESDAY	THURSDAY	FRIDAY	SATURDAY	SUNDAY
30	31	1	2	3	4	5 ○
6	7	8	9	10	11	12
13 ☾	14	15	16	17	18	19
20 ●	21	22	23	24	25	26
27 ☽	28	1	2	3	4	5

MARCH – 2023 MONTH PLANNER

MONDAY	TUESDAY	WEDNESDAY	THURSDAY	FRIDAY	SATURDAY	SUNDAY
27 ☽	28	1	2	3	4	5
6	7 ○	8	9	10	11	12
13	14	15 ☾	16	17	18	19
20 ✿	21 ●	22	23	24	25	26 ☉
27	28	29 ☽	30	31	1	2

APRIL – 2023 MONTH PLANNER

MONDAY	TUESDAY	WEDNESDAY	THURSDAY	FRIDAY	SATURDAY	SUNDAY
27	28	29 ☽	30	31	1	2
3	4	5	6 ○	7	8	9
10	11	12	13 ☾	14	15	16
17	18	19	20 ●	21	22	23
24	25	26	27 ☽	28	29	30

MAY – 2023 MONTH PLANNER

MONDAY	TUESDAY	WEDNESDAY	THURSDAY	FRIDAY	SATURDAY	SUNDAY
1	2	3	4	5 ○	6	7
8	9	10	11	12 ☾	13	14
15	16	17	18	19 ●	20	21
22	23	24	25	26	27 ☽	28
29	30	31	1	2	3	4 ○

JUNE – 2023 MONTH PLANNER

MONDAY	TUESDAY	WEDNESDAY	THURSDAY	FRIDAY	SATURDAY	SUNDAY
29	30	31	1	2	3	4 ○
5	6	7	8	9	10 ☾	11
12	13	14	15	16	17	18 ●
19	20	21 ☀	22	23	24	25
26 ☽	27	28	29	30	1	2

JULY – 2023 MONTH PLANNER

MONDAY	TUESDAY	WEDNESDAY	THURSDAY	FRIDAY	SATURDAY	SUNDAY
26 ☽	27	28	29	30	1	2
3 ○	4	5	6	7	8	9
10 ☾	11	12	13	14	15	16
17 ●	18	19	20	21	22	23
24 / 31	25 ☽	26	27	28	29	30

AUGUST – 2023 MONTH PLANNER

MONDAY	TUESDAY	WEDNESDAY	THURSDAY	FRIDAY	SATURDAY	SUNDAY
31	1	○ 2	3	4	5	6
7	8	☾ 9	10	11	12	13
14	15	16 ●	17	18	19	20
21	22	23	24 ☽	25	26	27
28	29	30	31 ○	1	2	3

SEPTEMBER – 2023 MONTH PLANNER

MONDAY	TUESDAY	WEDNESDAY	THURSDAY	FRIDAY	SATURDAY	SUNDAY
28	29	30	31 ○	1	2	3
4	5	6 ☾	7	8	9	10
11	12	13	14	15 ●	16	17
18	19	20	21	22 ☽	23	24
25	26	27	28	29 ○	30	1

OCTOBER – 2023 MONTH PLANNER

MONDAY	TUESDAY	WEDNESDAY	THURSDAY	FRIDAY	SATURDAY	SUNDAY
25	26	27	28	29 ○	30	1
2	3	4	5	6 ☾	7	8
9	10	11	12	13	14 ●	15
16	17	18	19	20	21	22 ☽
23	24	25	26	27	28 ○	29
30	31					

NOVEMBER – 2023 MONTH PLANNER

MONDAY	TUESDAY	WEDNESDAY	THURSDAY	FRIDAY	SATURDAY	SUNDAY
30	31	1	2	3	4	5 ☾
6	7	8	9	10	11	12
13 ●	14	15	16	17	18	19
20 ☽	21	22	23	24	25	26
27 ○	28	29	30	1	2	3

DECEMBER – 2023 MONTH PLANNER

MONDAY	TUESDAY	WEDNESDAY	THURSDAY	FRIDAY	SATURDAY	SUNDAY
27 ○	28	29	30	1	2	3
4	5 ☾	6	7	8	9	10
11	12 ●	13	14	15	16	17
18	19 ☽	20	21	22 ✸	23	24
25	26	27 ○	28	29	30	31

NOTES

NOTES

THE YEAR
2023

26 MON

27 TUE

28 WED

29 THU

30 FRI ☽

31 SAT

1 SUN

DECEMBER

	M	T	W	T	F	S	**S**
48	28	29	30	1	2	3	**4**
49	5	6	7	8	9	10	**11**
50	12	13	14	15	16	17	**18**
51	19	20	21	22	23	24	**25**
52	26	27	28	29	30	31	1

2 MON

3 TUE

4 WED

5 THU

6 FRI ○

7 SAT

8 SUN

JANUARY

	M	T	W	T	F	S	**S**
52	26	27	28	29	30	31	**1**
1	2	3	4	5	6	7	**8**
2	9	10	11	12	13	14	**15**
3	16	17	18	19	20	21	**22**
4	$^{23}/_{30}$ $^{24}/_{31}$	25	26	27	28	**29**

9 MON

---

10 TUE

---

11 WED

---

12 THU

---

13 FRI

---

14 SAT

---

15 SUN ☾

JANUARY

	M	T	W	T	F	S	**S**
52	26	27	28	29	30	31	**1**
1	2	3	4	5	6	7	**8**
2	9	10	11	12	13	14	**15**
3	16	17	18	19	20	21	**22**
4	23/30 24/31	25	26	27	28	**29**

16 MON

17 TUE

18 WED

19 THU

20 FRI

21 SAT ●

22 SUN

JANUARY

	M	T	W	T	F	S	**S**
52	26	27	28	29	30	31	**1**
1	2	3	4	5	6	7	**8**
2	9	10	11	12	13	14	**15**
3	16	17	18	19	20	21	**22**
4	$^{23}/_{30}$ $^{24}/_{31}$	25	26	27	28	**29**

23 MON

---

24 TUE

---

25 WED

---

26 THU

---

27 FRI

---

28 SAT ☽

---

29 SUN

---

30 MON

31 TUE

1 WED

2 THU

3 FRI

4 SAT

5 SUN ○

FEBRUARY						
M	T	W	T	F	S	**S**
5	30	31	1	2	3	4	**5**
6	6	7	8	9	10	11	**12**
7	13	14	15	16	17	18	**19**
8	20	21	22	23	24	25	**26**
9	27	28	1	2	3	4	5

6 MON

7 TUE

8 WED

9 THU

10 FRI

11 SAT

12 SUN

FEBRUARY

	M	T	W	T	F	S	**S**
5	30	31	1	2	3	4	**5**
6	6	7	8	9	10	11	**12**
7	13	14	15	16	17	18	**19**
8	20	21	22	23	24	25	**26**
9	27	28	1	2	3	4	5

13 MON ☽

14 TUE

15 WED

16 THU

17 FRI

18 SAT

19 SUN

FEBRUARY

	M	T	W	T	F	S	**S**
5	30	31	1	2	3	4	**5**
6	6	7	8	9	10	11	**12**
7	13	14	15	16	17	18	**19**
8	20	21	22	23	24	25	**26**
9	27	28	1	2	3	4	5

20 MON ●

21 TUE

22 WED

23 THU

24 FRI

25 SAT

26 SUN

FEBRUARY

	M	T	W	T	F	S	**S**
5	30	31	1	2	3	4	**5**
6	6	7	8	9	10	11	**12**
7	13	14	15	16	17	18	**19**
8	20	21	22	23	24	25	**26**
9	27	28	1	2	3	4	5

27 MON ☽

28 TUE

1 WED

2 THU

3 FRI

4 SAT

5 SUN

MARCH

	M	T	W	T	F	S	**S**
9	27	28	1	2	3	4	**5**
10	6	7	8	9	10	11	**12**
11	13	14	15	16	17	18	**19**
12	20	21	22	23	24	25	**26**
13	27	28	29	30	31	1	2

6 MON

7 TUE ○

8 WED

9 THU

10 FRI

11 SAT

12 SUN

MARCH

	M	T	W	T	F	S	**S**
9	27	28	1	2	3	4	**5**
10	6	7	8	9	10	11	**12**
11	13	14	15	16	17	18	**19**
12	20	21	22	23	24	25	**26**
13	27	28	29	30	31	1	2

13 MON

14 TUE

15 WED ☾

16 THU

17 FRI

18 SAT

19 SUN

MARCH						
	M	T	W	T	F	S	**S**
9	27	28	1	2	3	4	**5**
10	6	7	8	9	10	11	**12**
11	13	14	15	16	17	18	**19**
12	20	21	22	23	24	25	**26**
13	27	28	29	30	31	1	2

20 MON
❀ 21:24 UTC

21 TUE ●

22 WED

23 THU

24 FRI

25 SAT

26 SUN ☺

MARCH

	M	T	W	T	F	S	**S**
9	27	28	1	2	3	4	**5**
10	6	7	8	9	10	11	**12**
11	13	14	15	16	17	18	**19**
12	20	21	22	23	24	25	**26**
13	27	28	29	30	31	1	2

27 MON

28 TUE

29 WED ☽

30 THU

31 FRI

1 SAT

2 SUN

MARCH

	M	T	W	T	F	S	**S**
9	27	28	1	2	3	4	**5**
10	6	7	8	9	10	11	**12**
11	13	14	15	16	17	18	**19**
12	20	21	22	23	24	25	**26**
13	27	28	29	30	31	1	2

3 MON

4 TUE

5 WED

6 THU ○

7 FRI

8 SAT

9 SUN

APRIL

	M	T	W	T	F	S	**S**
13	27	28	29	30	31	1	**2**
14	3	4	5	6	7	8	**9**
15	10	11	12	13	14	15	**16**
16	17	18	19	20	21	22	**23**
17	24	25	26	27	28	29	**30**

10 MON

11 TUE

12 WED

13 THU ☾

14 FRI

15 SAT

16 SUN

APRIL

M T W T F S **S**

13 27 28 29 30 31 1 **2**

14 3 4 5 6 7 8 **9**

15 10 11 12 13 14 15 **16**

16 17 18 19 20 21 22 **23**

17 24 25 26 27 28 29 **30**

17 MON

18 TUE

19 WED

20 THU ●

21 FRI

22 SAT

23 SUN

APRIL

	M	T	W	T	F	S	**S**
13	27	28	29	30	31	1	**2**
14	3	4	5	6	7	8	**9**
15	10	11	12	13	14	15	**16**
16	17	18	19	20	21	22	**23**
17	24	25	26	27	28	29	**30**

24 MON

25 TUE

26 WED

27 THU ☽

28 FRI

29 SAT

30 SUN

APRIL

	M	T	W	T	F	S	**S**
13	27	28	29	30	31	1	**2**
14	3	4	5	6	7	8	**9**
15	10	11	12	13	14	15	**16**
16	17	18	19	20	21	22	**23**
17	24	25	26	27	28	29	**30**

1 MON

2 TUE

3 WED

4 THU

5 FRI ○

6 SAT

7 SUN

	M	T	W	T	F	S	**S**
18	1	2	3	4	5	6	**7**
19	8	9	10	11	12	13	**14**
20	15	16	17	18	19	20	**21**
21	22	23	24	25	26	27	**28**
22	29	30	31	1	2	3	4

MAY

8 MON

9 TUE

10 WED

11 THU

12 FRI ☾

13 SAT

14 SUN

MAY

	M	T	W	T	F	S	**S**
18	1	2	3	4	5	6	**7**
19	8	9	10	11	12	13	**14**
20	15	16	17	18	19	20	**21**
21	22	23	24	25	26	27	**28**
22	29	30	31	1	2	3	4

15 MON

16 TUE

17 WED

18 THU

19 FRI ●

20 SAT

21 SUN

MAY

	M	T	W	T	F	S	**S**
18	1	2	3	4	5	6	**7**
19	8	9	10	11	12	13	**14**
20	15	16	17	18	19	20	**21**
21	22	23	24	25	26	27	**28**
22	29	30	31	1	2	3	4

22 MON

23 TUE

24 WED

25 THU

26 FRI

27 SAT ☽

28 SUN

MAY

	M	T	W	T	F	S	**S**
18	1	2	3	4	5	6	**7**
19	8	9	10	11	12	13	**14**
20	15	16	17	18	19	20	**21**
21	22	23	24	25	26	27	**28**
22	29	30	31	1	2	3	4

29 MON

30 TUE

31 WED

1 THU

2 FRI

3 SAT

4 SUN ○

JUNE

	M	T	W	T	F	S	**S**
22	29	30	31	1	2	3	**4**
23	5	6	7	8	9	10	**11**
24	12	13	14	15	16	17	**18**
25	19	20	21	22	23	24	**25**
26	26	27	28	29	30	1	2

5 MON

6 TUE

7 WED

8 THU

9 FRI

10 SAT ☾

11 SUN

JUNE

	M	T	W	T	F	S	**S**
22	29	30	31	1	2	3	**4**
23	5	6	7	8	9	10	**11**
24	12	13	14	15	16	17	**18**
25	19	20	21	22	23	24	**25**
26	26	27	28	29	30	1	2

12 MON

13 TUE

14 WED

15 THU

16 FRI

17 SAT

18 SUN ●

		JUNE				
	M	T	W	T	F	S	**S**
22	29	30	31	1	2	3	**4**
23	5	6	7	8	9	10	**11**
24	12	13	14	15	16	17	**18**
25	19	20	21	22	23	24	**25**
26	26	27	28	29	30	1	2

19 MON

20 TUE

21 WED
☼ 14:58 UTC

22 THU

23 FRI

24 SAT

25 SUN

JUNE

	M	T	W	T	F	S	**S**
22	29	30	31	1	2	3	**4**
23	5	6	7	8	9	10	**11**
24	12	13	14	15	16	17	**18**
25	19	20	21	22	23	24	**25**
26	26	27	28	29	30	1	2

26 MON ☽

27 TUE

28 WED

29 THU

30 FRI

1 SAT

2 SUN

JUNE

	M	T	W	T	F	S	**S**
22	29	30	31	1	2	3	**4**
23	5	6	7	8	9	10	**11**
24	12	13	14	15	16	17	**18**
25	19	20	21	22	23	24	**25**
26	26	27	28	29	30	1	2

3 MON ○

4 TUE

5 WED

6 THU

7 FRI

8 SAT

9 SUN

JULY

	M	T	W	T	F	S	**S**
26	26	27	28	29	30	1	**2**
27	3	4	5	6	7	8	**9**
28	10	11	12	13	14	15	**16**
29	17	18	19	20	21	22	**23**
30	24/31	25	26	27	28	29	**30**

10 MON ☾

11 TUE

12 WED

13 THU

14 FRI

15 SAT

16 SUN

JULY

M	T	W	T	F	S	**S**
26	26	27	28	29	30	1	**2**
27	3	4	5	6	7	8	**9**
28	10	11	12	13	14	15	**16**
29	17	18	19	20	21	22	**23**
30	24/31	25	26	27	28	29	**30**

17 MON ●

18 TUE

19 WED

20 THU

21 FRI

22 SAT

23 SUN

JULY

M	T	W	T	F	S	**S**
26	26	27	28	29	30	1	**2**
27	3	4	5	6	7	8	**9**
28	10	11	12	13	14	15	**16**
29	17	18	19	20	21	22	**23**
30	²⁴/₃₁	25	26	27	28	29	**30**

24 MON

25 TUE ☽

26 WED

27 THU

28 FRI

29 SAT

30 SUN

JULY

	M	T	W	T	F	S	**S**
26	26	27	28	29	30	1	**2**
27	3	4	5	6	7	8	**9**
28	10	11	12	13	14	15	**16**
29	17	18	19	20	21	22	**23**
30	24/31	25	26	27	28	29	**30**

31 MON

1 TUE ○

2 WED

3 THU

4 FRI

5 SAT

6 SUN

AUGUST

	M	T	W	T	F	S	**S**
31	31	1	2	3	4	5	**6**
32	7	8	9	10	11	12	**13**
33	14	15	16	17	18	19	**20**
34	21	22	23	24	25	26	**27**
35	28	29	30	31	1	2	3

7 MON

8 TUE ☾

9 WED

10 THU

11 FRI

12 SAT

13 SUN

AUGUST

	M	T	W	T	F	S	**S**
31	31	1	2	3	4	5	**6**
32	7	8	9	10	11	12	**13**
33	14	15	16	17	18	19	**20**
34	21	22	23	24	25	26	**27**
35	28	29	30	31	1	2	3

14 MON

15 TUE

16 WED ●

17 THU

18 FRI

19 SAT

20 SUN

AUGUST

	M	T	W	T	F	S	**S**
31	31	1	2	3	4	5	**6**
32	7	8	9	10	11	12	**13**
33	14	15	16	17	18	19	**20**
34	21	22	23	24	25	26	**27**
35	28	29	30	31	1	2	3

21 MON

22 TUE

23 WED

24 THU 🌙

25 FRI

26 SAT

27 SUN

AUGUST

	M	T	W	T	F	S	**S**
31	31	1	2	3	4	5	**6**
32	7	8	9	10	11	12	**13**
33	14	15	16	17	18	19	**20**
34	21	22	23	24	25	26	**27**
35	28	29	30	31	1	2	3

28 MON

29 TUE

30 WED

31 THU ○

1 FRI

2 SAT

3 SUN

AUGUST

	M	T	W	T	F	S	**S**
31	31	1	2	3	4	5	**6**
32	7	8	9	10	11	12	**13**
33	14	15	16	17	18	19	**20**
34	21	22	23	24	25	26	**27**
35	28	29	30	31	1	2	3

4 MON

5 TUE

6 WED ☾

7 THU

8 FRI

9 SAT

10 SUN

SEPTEMBER

	M	T	W	T	F	S	**S**
35	28	29	30	31	1	2	**3**
36	4	5	6	7	8	9	**10**
37	11	12	13	14	15	16	**17**
38	18	19	20	21	22	23	**24**
39	25	26	27	28	29	30	1

11 MON

12 TUE

13 WED

14 THU

15 FRI ●

16 SAT

17 SUN

SEPTEMBER

	M	T	W	T	F	S	**S**
35	28	29	30	31	1	2	**3**
36	4	5	6	7	8	9	**10**
37	11	12	13	14	15	16	**17**
38	18	19	20	21	22	23	**24**
39	25	26	27	28	29	30	1

18 MON

19 TUE

20 WED

21 THU

22 FRI ☽

23 SAT

🕊 06:50 UTC

24 SUN

SEPTEMBER

	M	T	W	T	F	S	**S**
35	28	29	30	31	1	2	**3**
36	4	5	6	7	8	9	**10**
37	11	12	13	14	15	16	**17**
38	18	19	20	21	22	23	**24**
39	25	26	27	28	29	30	1

25 MON

26 TUE

27 WED

28 THU

29 FRI ○

30 SAT

1 SUN

SEPTEMBER

	M	T	W	T	F	S	**S**
35	28	29	30	31	1	2	**3**
36	4	5	6	7	8	9	**10**
37	11	12	13	14	15	16	**17**
38	18	19	20	21	22	23	**24**
39	25	26	27	28	29	30	1

2 MON

3 TUE

4 WED

5 THU

6 FRI ☾

7 SAT

8 SUN

OCTOBER

	M	T	W	T	F	S	**S**
39	25	26	27	28	29	30	**1**
40	2	3	4	5	6	7	**8**
41	9	10	11	12	13	14	**15**
42	16	17	18	19	20	21	**22**
43	$^{23}/_{30}$ $^{24}/_{31}$	25	26	27	28	**29**

9 MON

10 TUE

11 WED

12 THU

13 FRI

14 SAT ●

15 SUN

OCTOBER

	M	T	W	T	F	S	**S**
39	25	26	27	28	29	30	**1**
40	2	3	4	5	6	7	**8**
41	9	10	11	12	13	14	**15**
42	16	17	18	19	20	21	**22**
43	23/30 24/31	25	26	27	28	**29**	

16 MON

---

17 TUE

---

18 WED

---

19 THU

---

20 FRI

---

21 SAT

---

22 SUN ☽

OCTOBER

	M	T	W	T	F	S	**S**
39	25	26	27	28	29	30	**1**
40	2	3	4	5	6	7	**8**
41	9	10	11	12	13	14	**15**
42	16	17	18	19	20	21	**22**
43	$^{23}/_{30}$ $^{24}/_{31}$	25	26	27	28	**29**

23 MON

24 TUE

25 WED

26 THU

27 FRI

28 SAT ○

29 SUN ◐

OCTOBER

	M	T	W	T	F	S	**S**
39	25	26	27	28	29	30	**1**
40	2	3	4	5	6	7	**8**
41	9	10	11	12	13	14	**15**
42	16	17	18	19	20	21	**22**
43	23/30 24/31	25	26	27	28	**29**

30 MON

31 TUE

1 WED

2 THU

3 FRI

4 SAT

5 SUN ☾

NOVEMBER

	M	T	W	T	F	S	**S**
44	30	31	1	2	3	4	**5**
45	6	7	8	9	10	11	**12**
46	13	14	15	16	17	18	**19**
47	20	21	22	23	24	25	**26**
48	27	28	29	30	1	2	3

6 MON

7 TUE

8 WED

9 THU

10 FRI

11 SAT

12 SUN

NOVEMBER

	M	T	W	T	F	S	**S**
44	30	31	1	2	3	4	**5**
45	6	7	8	9	10	11	**12**
46	13	14	15	16	17	18	**19**
47	20	21	22	23	24	25	**26**
48	27	28	29	30	1	2	3

13 MON ●

14 TUE

15 WED

16 THU

17 FRI

18 SAT

19 SUN

NOVEMBER

	M	T	W	T	F	S	**S**
44	30	31	1	2	3	4	**5**
45	6	7	8	9	10	11	**12**
46	13	14	15	16	17	18	**19**
47	20	21	22	23	24	25	**26**
48	27	28	29	30	1	2	3

20 MON ☽

---

21 TUE

---

22 WED

---

23 THU

---

24 FRI

---

25 SAT

---

26 SUN

NOVEMBER

	M	T	W	T	F	S	**S**
44	30	31	1	2	3	4	**5**
45	6	7	8	9	10	11	**12**
46	13	14	15	16	17	18	**19**
47	20	21	22	23	24	25	**26**
48	27	28	29	30	1	2	3

27 MON ○

28 TUE

29 WED

30 THU

1 FRI

2 SAT

3 SUN

NOVEMBER

	M	T	W	T	F	S	**S**
44	30	31	1	2	3	4	**5**
45	6	7	8	9	10	11	**12**
46	13	14	15	16	17	18	**19**
47	20	21	22	23	24	25	**26**
48	27	28	29	30	1	2	3

4 MON

5 TUE ☾

6 WED

7 THU

8 FRI

9 SAT

10 SUN

DECEMBER

	M	T	W	T	F	S	**S**
48	27	28	29	30	1	2	**3**
49	4	5	6	7	8	9	**10**
50	11	12	13	14	15	16	**17**
51	18	19	20	21	22	23	**24**
52	25	26	27	28	29	30	**31**

11 MON

12 TUE ●

13 WED

14 THU

15 FRI

16 SAT

17 SUN

18 MON

19 TUE ☽

20 WED

21 THU

22 FRI
☀ 03:27 UTC

23 SAT

24 SUN

DECEMBER

	M	T	W	T	F	S	**S**
48	27	28	29	30	1	2	**3**
49	4	5	6	7	8	9	**10**
50	11	12	13	14	15	16	**17**
51	18	19	20	21	22	23	**24**
52	25	26	27	28	29	30	**31**

25 MON

_____

26 TUE

_____

27 WED ○

_____

28 THU

_____

29 FRI

_____

30 SAT

_____

31 SUN

_____

DECEMBER

	M	T	W	T	F	S	**S**
48	27	28	29	30	1	2	**3**
49	4	5	6	7	8	9	**10**
50	11	12	13	14	15	16	**17**
51	18	19	20	21	22	23	**24**
52	25	26	27	28	29	30	**31**

INTERNATIONAL HOLIDAYS 2024

AUSTRALIA

January 1	New Year's Day
26	Australia Day
March 29	Good Friday
30	Easter Saturday*
31	Easter
April 1	Easter Monday
25	Anzac Day
June 10	Queen's Birthday*
December 25	Christmas Day
26	Boxing Day

AUSTRIA

January 1	New Year's Day
6	Epiphany
March 29	Good Friday*
31	Easter
April 1	Easter Monday
May 1	Labour Day
9	Ascension
20	Whit Monday
30	Corpus Christi Day
August 15	Assumption
October 26	National Day
November 1	All Saints' Day
December 8	Immaculate Conception
25	Christmas Day
26	St Stephen's Day

BELGIUM

January 1	New Year's Day
March 31	Easter
April 1	Easter Monday
May 1	Labour Day
9	Ascension
20	Whit Monday
July 21	National Day
August 15	Assumption
November 1	All Saints' Day
11	Armistice Day
December 25	Christmas Day

CANADA

January 1	New Year's Day
February 19	Civic Holiday*
March 29	Good Friday
31	Easter
May 20	Victoria Day
July 1	Canada Day
August 5	Civic Holiday*
September 2	Labour Day
October 14	Thanksgiving Day
November 11	Remembrance Day

December 25	Christmas Day
26	Boxing Day

CZECH REPUBLIC

January 1	New Year's Day
March 29	Good Friday
31	Easter
April 1	Easter Monday
May 1	May Day
8	Liberation Day
July 5	St Cyril and St Methodius Day
6	Jan Hus Day
September 28	Statehood Day
October 28	Independence Day
November 17	Freedom and Democracy Day
December 24	Christmas Eve
25	Christmas Day
26	Second Christmas Day

FRANCE

January 1	New Year's Day
March 31	Easter
April 1	Easter Monday
May 1	Labour Day
8	WWII Victory Day
9	Ascension
20	Whit Monday
July 14	National Day
August 15	Assumption
November 1	All Saints' Day
11	Armistice Day
December 25	Christmas Day

GERMANY

January 1	New Year's Day
March 29	Good Friday
31	Easter
April 1	Easter Monday
May 1	Labour Day
9	Ascension
20	Whit Monday
October 3	Day of German Unity
December 25	Christmas Day
26	Second Christmas Day

IRELAND

January 1	New Year's Day
March 17	St Patrick's Day
29	Good Friday
31	Easter
April 1	Easter Monday
May 6	May Bank Holiday
June 3	June Bank Holiday
August 5	August Bank Holiday
October 28	October Bank Holiday

INTERNATIONAL HOLIDAYS 2024

December 25 Christmas Day
26 St Stephen's Day

ITALY
January 1 New Year's Day
6 Epiphany
March 31 Easter
April 1 Easter Monday
25 Liberation Day
May 1 Labour Day
June 2 Republic Day
August 15 Assumption
November 1 All Saints' Day
December 8 Immaculate Conception
25 Christmas Day
26 St Stephen's Day

JAPAN
January 1 New Year's Day
8 Coming of Age Day
February 11 National Foundation Day
23 Emperor's Birthday
March 20 Vernal Equinox Day
April 29 Showa Day
May 3 Constitution Memorial Day
4 Greenery Day
5 Children's Day
July 15 Marine Day
August 11 Mountain Day
September 16 Respect for the Aged Day
22 Autumnal Equinox Day
October 14 Sports Day
November 3 Culture Day
23 Labour Thanksgiving Day

NETHERLANDS
January 1 New Year's Day
March 29 Good Friday*
31 Easter
April 1 Easter Monday
27 King's Birthday
May 5 Liberation Day
9 Ascension
19 Pentecost
20 Whit Monday
December 25 Christmas Day
26 Second Christmas Day

NORWAY
January 1 New Year's Day
March 28 Maundy Thursday
29 Good Friday
31 Easter
April 1 Easter Monday
May 1 Labour Day

9 Ascension
17 Constitution Day
19 Whit Sunday
20 Whit Monday
December 25 Christmas Day
26 Second Christmas Day

POLAND
January 1 New Year's Day
6 Epiphany
March 31 Easter
April 1 Easter Monday
May 1 State Holiday
3 Constitution Day
19 Pentecost
30 Corpus Christi Day
August 15 Assumption
November 1 All Saints' Day
11 Independence Day
December 25 Christmas Day
26 Second Christmas Day

PORTUGAL
January 1 New Year's Day
February 13 Shrove Tuesday (Carnival)
March 29 Good Friday
31 Easter
April 25 Liberation Day
May 1 Labour Day
30 Corpus Christi Day
June 10 National Day
August 15 Assumption
October 5 Republic Day
November 1 All Saints' Day
December 1 Independence Day
8 Immaculate Conception
25 Christmas Day

SLOVAKIA
January 1 New Year's Day
Republic Day
6 Epiphany
March 29 Good Friday
31 Easter
April 1 Easter Monday
May 1 May Day
8 Victory Day
July 5 St Cyril and St Methodius Day
August 29 Slovak National Uprising Day
September 1 Constitution Day
15 Our Lady of Sorrows Day
November 1 All Saints' Day
17 Freedom and Democracy Day
December 24 Christmas Eve

INTERNATIONAL HOLIDAYS 2024

25 Christmas Day
26 Second Christmas Day

SPAIN
January 1 New Year's Day
6 Epiphany
March 28 Maundy Thursday*
29 Good Friday
May 1 Labour Day
August 15 Assumption
October 12 National Day
November 1 All Saints' Day
December 6 Constitution Day
8 Immaculate Conception
25 Christmas Day

SWEDEN
January 1 New Year's Day
6 Epiphany
March 29 Good Friday
31 Easter
April 1 Easter Monday
May 1 Labour Day
9 Ascension
19 Pentecost
June 6 National Day
22 Midsummer's Day
November 2 All Saints' Day
December 25 Christmas Day
26 Second Christmas Day

SWITZERLAND
January 1 New Year's Day
March 29 Good Friday*
31 Easter

April 1 Easter Monday*
May 1 Labour Day*
9 Ascension
20 Whit Monday*
August 1 National Day
December 25 Christmas Day
26 St Stephen's Day*

UNITED KINGDOM
January 1 New Year's Day
2 Second of January*
March 17 St Patrick's Day*
29 Good Friday
31 Easter
April 1 Easter Monday*
May 6 Early May Bank Holiday
27 Spring Bank Holiday
August 5 Summer Bank Holiday*
26 Summer Bank Holiday*
November 30 St Andrew's Day*
December 25 Christmas Day
26 Boxing Day

USA
January 1 New Year's Day
15 Martin Luther King Jr Day
February 19 Presidents' Day
March 31 Easter
May 27 Memorial Day
July 4 Independence Day
September 2 Labour Day
October 14 Columbus Day
November 11 Veterans' Day
28 Thanksgiving Day
December 25 Christmas Day

Not a public holiday/Not a public holiday in all regions.
This table lists commemorative dates. Additional public holidays may precede or follow some dates.
Regional holidays may not be included. This information is provided as a guide only.

NOTES

NOTES

2024

JANUARY

M	T	W	T	F	S	**S**
1	2	3	4	5	6	**7**
8	9	10	11	12	13	**14**
15	16	17	18	19	20	**21**
22	23	24	25	26	27	**28**
29	30	31	1	2	3	4

FEBRUARY

M	T	W	T	F	S	**S**
29	30	31	1	2	3	**4**
5	6	7	8	9	10	**11**
12	13	14	15	16	17	**18**
19	20	21	22	23	24	**25**
26	27	28	29	1	2	3

MARCH

M	T	W	T	F	S	**S**
26	27	28	29	1	2	**3**
4	5	6	7	8	9	**10**
11	12	13	14	15	16	**17**
18	19	20	21	22	23	**24**
25	26	27	28	29	30	**31**

APRIL

M	T	W	T	F	S	**S**
1	2	3	4	5	6	**7**
8	9	10	11	12	13	**14**
15	16	17	18	19	20	**21**
22	23	24	25	26	27	**28**
29	30	1	2	3	4	5

MAY

M	T	W	T	F	S	**S**
29	30	1	2	3	4	**5**
6	7	8	9	10	11	**12**
13	14	15	16	17	18	**19**
20	21	22	23	24	25	**26**
27	28	29	30	31	1	2

JUNE

M	T	W	T	F	S	**S**
27	28	29	30	31	1	**2**
3	4	5	6	7	8	**9**
10	11	12	13	14	15	**16**
17	18	19	20	21	22	**23**
24	25	26	27	28	29	**30**

JULY

M	T	W	T	F	S	**S**
1	2	3	4	5	6	**7**
8	9	10	11	12	13	**14**
15	16	17	18	19	20	**21**
22	23	24	25	26	27	**28**
29	30	31	1	2	3	4

AUGUST

M	T	W	T	F	S	**S**
29	30	31	1	2	3	**4**
5	6	7	8	9	10	**11**
12	13	14	15	16	17	**18**
19	20	21	22	23	24	**25**
26	27	28	29	30	31	1

SEPTEMBER

M	T	W	T	F	S	**S**
26	27	28	29	30	31	**1**
2	3	4	5	6	7	**8**
9	10	11	12	13	14	**15**
16	17	18	19	20	21	**22**
$^{23}/_{30}$	24	25	26	27	28	**29**

OCTOBER

M	T	W	T	F	S	**S**
30	1	2	3	4	5	**6**
7	8	9	10	11	12	**13**
14	15	16	17	18	19	**20**
21	22	23	24	25	26	**27**
28	29	30	31	1	2	3

NOVEMBER

M	T	W	T	F	S	**S**
28	29	30	31	1	2	**3**
4	5	6	7	8	9	**10**
11	12	13	14	15	16	**17**
18	19	20	21	22	23	**24**
25	26	27	28	29	30	1

DECEMBER

M	T	W	T	F	S	**S**
25	26	27	28	29	30	**1**
2	3	4	5	6	7	**8**
9	10	11	12	13	14	**15**
16	17	18	19	20	21	**22**
$^{23}/_{30}$	$^{24}/_{31}$	25	26	27	28	**29**

NOTES

2025

JANUARY

M	T	W	T	F	S	**S**
30	31	1	2	3	4	**5**
6	7	8	9	10	11	**12**
13	14	15	16	17	18	**19**
20	21	22	23	24	25	**26**
27	28	29	30	31	1	2

FEBRUARY

M	T	W	T	F	S	**S**
27	28	29	30	31	1	**2**
3	4	5	6	7	8	**9**
10	11	12	13	14	15	**16**
17	18	19	20	21	22	**23**
24	25	26	27	28	1	2

MARCH

M	T	W	T	F	S	**S**
24	25	26	27	28	1	**2**
3	4	5	6	7	8	**9**
10	11	12	13	14	15	**16**
17	18	19	20	21	22	**23**
24/31	25	26	27	28	29	**30**

APRIL

M	T	W	T	F	S	**S**
31	1	2	3	4	5	**6**
7	8	9	10	11	12	**13**
14	15	16	17	18	19	**20**
21	22	23	24	25	26	**27**
28	29	30	1	2	3	4

MAY

M	T	W	T	F	S	**S**
28	29	30	1	2	3	**4**
5	6	7	8	9	10	**11**
12	13	14	15	16	17	**18**
19	20	21	22	23	24	**25**
26	27	28	29	30	31	1

JUNE

M	T	W	T	F	S	**S**
26	27	28	29	30	31	**1**
2	3	4	5	6	7	**8**
9	10	11	12	13	14	**15**
16	17	18	19	20	21	**22**
23/30	24	25	26	27	28	**29**

JULY

M	T	W	T	F	S	**S**
30	1	2	3	4	5	**6**
7	8	9	10	11	12	**13**
14	15	16	17	18	19	**20**
21	22	23	24	25	26	**27**
28	29	30	31	1	2	3

AUGUST

M	T	W	T	F	S	**S**
28	29	30	31	1	2	**3**
4	5	6	7	8	9	**10**
11	12	13	14	15	16	**17**
18	19	20	21	22	23	**24**
25	26	27	28	29	30	**31**

SEPTEMBER

M	T	W	T	F	S	**S**
1	2	3	4	5	6	**7**
8	9	10	11	12	13	**14**
15	16	17	18	19	20	**21**
22	23	24	25	26	27	**28**
29	30	1	2	3	4	5

OCTOBER

M	T	W	T	F	S	**S**
29	30	1	2	3	4	**5**
6	7	8	9	10	11	**12**
13	14	15	16	17	18	**19**
20	21	22	23	24	25	**26**
27	28	29	30	31	1	2

NOVEMBER

M	T	W	T	F	S	**S**
27	28	29	30	31	1	**2**
3	4	5	6	7	8	**9**
10	11	12	13	14	15	**16**
17	18	19	20	21	22	**23**
24	25	26	27	28	29	**30**

DECEMBER

M	T	W	T	F	S	**S**
1	2	3	4	5	6	**7**
8	9	10	11	12	13	**14**
15	16	17	18	19	20	**21**
22	23	24	25	26	27	**28**
29	30	31	1	2	3	4

NOTES

JANUARY – 2024 MONTH PLANNER

MONDAY	TUESDAY	WEDNESDAY	THURSDAY	FRIDAY	SATURDAY	SUNDAY
1	2	3	4 ☾	5	6	7
8	9	10	11 ●	12	13	14
15	16	17	18 ☽	19	20	21
22	23	24	25 ○	26	27	28
29	30	31	1	2 ☾	3	4

FEBRUARY – 2024 MONTH PLANNER

MONDAY	TUESDAY	WEDNESDAY	THURSDAY	FRIDAY	SATURDAY	SUNDAY
29	30	31	1	2 ☾	3	4
5	6	7	8	9 ●	10	11
12	13	14	15	16 ☽	17	18
19	20	21	22	23	24 ○	25
26	27	28	29	1	2	3 ☾

MARCH – 2024 MONTH PLANNER

MONDAY	TUESDAY	WEDNESDAY	THURSDAY	FRIDAY	SATURDAY	SUNDAY
26	27	28	29	1	2	3 ☾
4	5	6	7	8	9	10 ●
11	12	13	14	15	16	17 ☽
18	19	20 ✿	21	22	23	24
25 ○	26	27	28	29	30	31 ◔

APRIL – 2024 MONTH PLANNER

MONDAY	TUESDAY	WEDNESDAY	THURSDAY	FRIDAY	SATURDAY	SUNDAY
1	2 ☾	3	4	5	6	7
8 ●	9	10	11	12	13	14
15 ☽	16	17	18	19	20	21
22	23 ○	24	25	26	27	28
29	30	1 ☾	2	3	4	5

MAY – 2024 MONTH PLANNER

MONDAY	TUESDAY	WEDNESDAY	THURSDAY	FRIDAY	SATURDAY	SUNDAY
29	30	1 ☾	2	3	4	5
6	7	8 ●	9	10	11	12
13	14	15 ☽	16	17	18	19
20	21	22	23 ○	24	25	26
27	28	29	30 ☾	31	1	2

JUNE – 2024 MONTH PLANNER

MONDAY	TUESDAY	WEDNESDAY	THURSDAY	FRIDAY	SATURDAY	SUNDAY
27	28	29	30 ☾	31	1	2
3	4	5	6 ●	7	8	9
10	11	12	13	14 ☽	15	16
17	18	19	20 ☀	21	22 ○	23
24	25	26	27	28 ☾	29	30

JULY – 2024 MONTH PLANNER

MONDAY	TUESDAY	WEDNESDAY	THURSDAY	FRIDAY	SATURDAY	SUNDAY
1	2	3	4	5 ●	6	7
8	9	10	11	12	13 ☽	14
15	16	17	18	19	20	21 ○
22	23	24	25	26	27	28 ☾
29	30	31	1	2	3	4 ●

AUGUST – 2024 MONTH PLANNER

MONDAY	TUESDAY	WEDNESDAY	THURSDAY	FRIDAY	SATURDAY	SUNDAY
29	30	31	1	2	3	4 ●
5	6	7	8	9	10	11
12 ☽	13	14	15	16	17	18
19 ○	20	21	22	23	24	25
26 ☾	27	28	29	30	31	1

SEPTEMBER – 2024 MONTH PLANNER

MONDAY	TUESDAY	WEDNESDAY	THURSDAY	FRIDAY	SATURDAY	SUNDAY
26 ☾	27	28	29	30	31	1
2	3 ●	4	5	6	7	8
9	10	11 ☽	12	13	14	15
16	17	18 ○	19	20	21	22
23 30	24 ☾	25	26	27	28	29

OCTOBER – 2024 MONTH PLANNER

MONDAY	TUESDAY	WEDNESDAY	THURSDAY	FRIDAY	SATURDAY	SUNDAY
30	1	2 ●	3	4	5	6
7	8	9	10 ☽	11	12	13
14	15	16	17 ○	18	19	20
21	22	23	24 ☾	25	26	27
28	29	30	31	1 ●	2	3

NOVEMBER – 2024 MONTH PLANNER

MONDAY	TUESDAY	WEDNESDAY	THURSDAY	FRIDAY	SATURDAY	SUNDAY
28	29	30	31	1 ●	2	3
4	5	6	7	8	9 ☽	10
11	12	13	14	15 ○	16	17
18	19	20	21	22	23 ☾	24
25	26	27	28	29	30	1 ●

DECEMBER – 2024 MONTH PLANNER

MONDAY	TUESDAY	WEDNESDAY	THURSDAY	FRIDAY	SATURDAY	SUNDAY
25	26	27	28	29	30	1 ●
2	3	4	5	6	7	8 ☽
9	10	11	12	13	14	15 ○
16	17	18	19	20	21 ☀	22 ☾
23	24	25	26	27	28	29
30 ●	31					

INTERNATIONAL DIALLING CODES

COUNTRY	DIAL OUT (ACCESS CODE)	DIAL IN (COUNTRY CODE)	EMERGENCY NUMBER	COUNTRY	DIAL OUT (ACCESS CODE)	DIAL IN (COUNTRY CODE)	EMERGENCY NUMBER
Algeria	00	213	17	Korea (South)	001*	82	999
Argentina	00	54	101	Latvia	00	371	112
Australia	0011	61	000	Lithuania	00	370	112
Austria	00	43	112	Luxembourg	00	352	112
Belgium	00	32	112	Macedonia	00	389	112
Bermuda	011	1441	911	Malaysia	00	60	999
Bolivia	00	591	110	Malta	00	356	112
Brazil	00	55	190	Mexico	00	52	066
Bulgaria	00	359	112	Morocco	00	212	19
Canada	011	1	911	Netherlands	00	31	112
Chile	00	56	133	New Zealand	00	64	111
China	00	86	110	Norway	00	47	112
Colombia	009*	57	112	Pakistan	00	92	15
Costa Rica	00	506	911	Paraguay	00	595	911
Croatia	00	385	112	Peru	00	51	105
Cuba	119	53	106	Philippines	00	63	117
Czech Republic	00	420	112	Poland	00	48	112
Denmark	00	45	112	Portugal	00	351	112
Dominican Republic	011	1809	911	Puerto Rico	011	1787*	911
Ecuador	00	593	911	Qatar	00	974	999
Egypt	00	20	122	Romania	00	40	112
Estonia	00	372	112	Russia	810	7	112
Finland	00*	358	112	Saudi Arabia	00	966	999
France	00	33	112	Slovakia	00	421	112
Georgia	00	995	112	Slovenia	00	386	112
Germany	00	49	112	South Africa	00	27	10111
Greece	00	30	112	Spain	00	34	112
Guatemala	00	502	110	Sweden	00	46	112
Honduras	00	504	199	Switzerland	00	41	112
Hungary	00	36	112	Syria	00	963	112
Iceland	00	354	112	Thailand	001	66	191
India	00	91	100	Tunisia	00	216	197
Iran	00	98	110	Turkey	00	90	155
Ireland (Republic)	00	353	112	U.A.E.	00	971	999
Israel	00*	972	100	Ukraine	00	380	112
Italy	00	39	112	United Kingdom	00	44	112
Jamaica	011	1876	119	United States	011	1	911
Japan	010	81	110	Uruguay	00	598	911
Jordan	00	962	911	Venezuela	00	58	171

*Additional access codes also in use.

WORLD TIME ZONES

UTC 12:00	UTC+1 13:00	UTC+2 14:00	UTC+3 15:00
Accra	Berlin	Athens	Baghdad
Lisbon	Paris	Cairo	Nairobi
London	Rome	Tel Aviv	Riyadh

UTC+4 16:00	UTC+5 17:00	UTC+5.5 17:30	UTC+6 18:00
Dubai	Karachi	Delhi	Almaty
Moscow	Tashkent	Kolkata	Dhaka
		Mumbai	

UTC+7 19:00	UTC+8 20:00	UTC+9 21:00	UTC+10 22:00
Bangkok	Beijing	Seoul	Melbourne
Jakarta	Manila	Tokyo	Sydney
	Singapore		

UTC+12 24:00	UTC−10 2:00	UTC−9 3:00	UTC−8 4:00
Auckland	Honolulu	Anchorage	Los Angeles
Suva			San Francisco
Wellington			Vancouver

UTC−6 6:00	UTC−5 7:00	UTC−4 8:00	UTC−3 9:00
Chicago	Miami	Halifax	Buenos Aires
Houston	New York	La Paz	Rio de Janeiro
Mexico City	Toronto	Santiago	

Coordinated Universal Time (UTC) is equivalent to Greenwich Mean Time (GMT).

CONVERSIONS

CLOTHING SIZES

WOMEN — CLOTHING							
France/Spain	34	36	38	40	42	44	46
Germany	32	34	36	38	40	42	44
Italy	36	38	40	42	44	46	48
Japan	5	7	9	11	13	15	17
North America	0	2	4	6	8	10	12
UK/Ireland	4	6	8	10	12	14	16
WOMEN — SHOES							
Europe	35	36	37	38	39	40	41
Japan	22	23	23.5	24	24.5	25.5	26
North America	5	6	6.5	7.5	8.5	9.5	10
UK/Ireland	2.5	3.5	4	5	6	7	7.5
MEN — SUITS AND COATS							
Europe	44	46	48	50	52	54	56
Japan	S	S	M	L	L	XL	XL
North America/UK/Ireland	34	36	38	40	42	44	46
MEN — SHOES							
Europe	40	41	42	43	44	45	46
Japan	25.5	26	26.5	27.5	28	29	29.5
North America	7.5	8	8.5	9.5	10	11	11.5
UK/Ireland	7	7.5	8	9	9.5	10.5	11

These measurements may vary between different countries and manufacturers. They are provided as a guide only.

MEASUREMENTS

WEIGHT		LENGTH/DISTANCE		AREA	
1 kilogram	2.2 pounds	1 centimetre	0.39 inches	1 sq metre	10.76 sq feet
1 pound	0.45 kilograms	1 inch	2.54 centimetres	1 sq foot	0.09 sq metres
1 kilogram	0.16 stone	1 metre	39.37 inches	1 sq metre	1.2 sq yards
1 stone	6.35 kilograms	1 foot	30.48 centimetres	1 sq yard	0.84 sq metres
VOLUME		1 kilometre	0.62 miles	1 hectare	2.47 acres
1 litre	0.26 gallons	1 mile	1.6 kilometres	1 acre	0.4 hectares
1 gallon (US)	3.78 litres	1 metre	1.09 yards		
1 gallon (US)	0.03 barrels	1 yard	91.44 centimetres		

TEMPERATURE

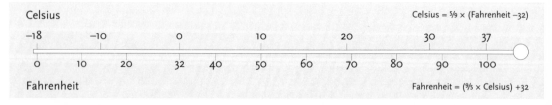

Celsius = ⅝ × (Fahrenheit −32)

Fahrenheit = (⅗ × Celsius) +32

TRAVEL PLANNING

DATE FROM/TO	DESTINATION

BIRTHDAYS & IMPORTANT DATES

DATE	EVENT

NOTES

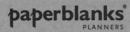

paperblanks®
PLANNERS

ENFER

Dante Alighieri (1265-1321) a composé la *Comédie Divine* sur une période de 12 ans, avant de la finir en 1320. Le poème est divisé en trois parties – *Enfer, Purgatoire* et *Paradis* – et c'est ici le premier chant de l'*Enfer* qui est reproduit. L'œuvre a joué un grand rôle dans la mise en place de la littérature italienne. Bien qu'aucun manuscrit original n'ait survécu, cette copie du XIVème siècle est l'une des plus.

INFERNO

Dante Alighieri (1265–1321) arbeitete 12 Jahre lang an der *Göttlichen Komödie* und stellte sie 1320 fertig. Er gliederte das Gedicht in drei Teile – *Inferno, Purgatorio* und *Paradiso* – und wir bilden hier den ersten Gesang aus *Inferno* ab. Die *Göttliche Komödie* war maßgeblich für die Entstehung der italienischen Literatur. Originalmanuskripte gibt es leider keine mehr. Diese Kopie aus dem 14. Jahrhundert zählt zu den frühesten Abschriften.

INFERNO

Dante Alighieri (1265-1321) compose la *Divina Commedia* in un periodo di dodici anni, completandola nel 1320. L'opera, fondamenta e massima espressione della letteratura italiana, è suddivisa in tre cantiche – *Inferno, Purgatorio* e *Paradiso* – composte da canti. La nostra copertina riproduce il primo canto dell'*Inferno*. Sebbene non si possieda il testo autografo dell'opera, questa copia del XIV secolo è una delle più antiche.

INFERNO

Dante Alighieri (1265-1321) dedicó doce años de su vida a escribir La Divina Comedia, que finalizó en 1320. Dividió el poema en tres partes: Infierno (cuyo primer canto reproducimos en nuestra cubierta), Purgatorio y Paraíso. La Divina Comedia es la obra maestra por excelencia de la literatura italiana. Este manuscrito original del siglo XIV es uno de los más antiguos que existen, si bien no se conserva ninguno del propio Dante.

EP0190

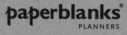

INFERNO

Dante Alighieri (1265–1321) composed the *Divine Comedy* over a period of 12 years, completing it in 1320. He divided the poem into three parts – *Inferno*, *Purgatorio* and *Paradiso* – and it is the first canto from *Inferno* that we have reproduced here. The *Divine Comedy* was instrumental in establishing the literature of Italy. Though no original manuscripts have survived, this 14th-century copy is one of the earliest produced.

AVAILABLE IN:
12-MONTH ULTRA HORIZONTAL
12-MONTH ULTRA VERTICAL
12-MONTH ULTRA VERSO

DESIGNED IN CANADA

Courtesy of De Agostini Picture Library/Bridgeman Images
Printed on acid-free, sustainable forest paper.
© 2020 Hartley & Marks Publishers Inc. All rights reserved.
No part of this book may be reproduced without written permission from the publisher.
Paperblanks are published by Hartley & Marks Publishers Inc. and
Hartley & Marks Publishers Ltd. Made in China.
North America 1-800-277-5887
Europe 800-3333-8005
Australia 1800-082-792

paperblanks.com